HEATHCLIFF BANQUET

by Geo Gately

tempo
books
GROSSET & DUNLAP
A Filmways Company
Publishers • New York

HEATHCLIFF BANQUET
Copyright ⓒ1973, 1974, 1975, 1977, 1980 McNaught
Syndicate, Inc.
All rights reserved
ISBN: 0-448-12634-6
A Tempo Books Original
Tempo Books is registered in the U.S. Patent Office
Published simultaneously in Canada
Printed in the United States of America

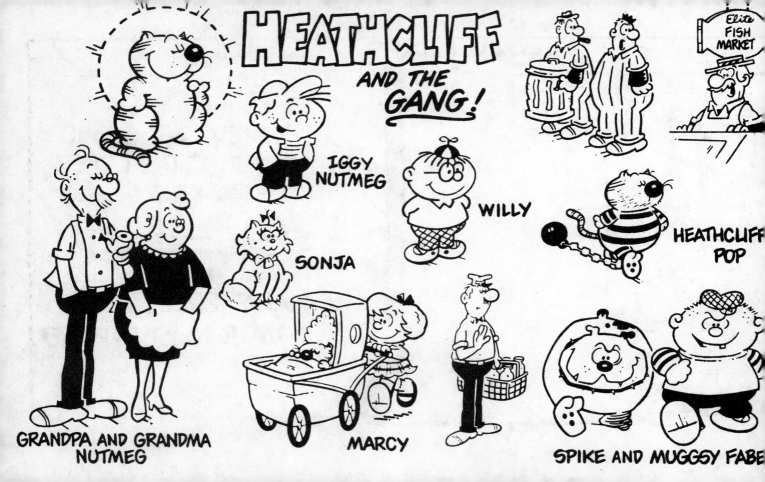

HEATHCLIFF
AND THE GANG!

IGGY NUTMEG

WILLY

SONJA

HEATHCLIFF POP

GRANDPA AND GRANDMA NUTMEG

MARCY

SPIKE AND MUGGSY FABE

WHEN IT ALL BEGAN...

SEPTEMBER 3RD, 1973
THE FIRST `HEATHCLIFF´ CARTOON!

"He's a winner!" ... Many reasons have been given for Heathcliff's popularity, but this seems to sum it up best. Through the years, cats have been depicted as either sinister or stupid, neither of which is true. Cats are smart! And so is Heathcliff! As you look through this book, you'll see how Heathcliff has evolved from the very first day through the years ... Enjoy!

"A VANILLA FUDGE SUNDAE AND A RAW FISH."

"WATCH THIS, GRAMPS...."

"HEATHCLIFF KNOWS THE EXACT LENGTH OF THAT LEASH!"

"WHAT HAPPENED TO HEATHCLIFF'S SCRATCHING POST?!"

"GRANDMA!"

9-6

"SCAT!"

© 1973
McNaught Synd., Inc.

9/7

"PLUS TWENTY DOLLARS DAMAGE IN THE
FROZEN FISH DEPARTMENT!"

"YOU'RE SITTING ON HIS DEAD MOUSE."

"CANNIBAL!"

"GET LOST!"

"YOU'D BETTER BELIEVE IT!"

"HEATHCLIFF HAS BEEN A VERY NAUGHTY
PUSSY CAT TODAY."

"I COULD HAVE SWORN SOMEONE TRIPPED ME!"

"ANY PETS?"

"YOU SAY YOU FOUND A LARGE, STRIPED, CANTANKEROUS TOM-CAT..."

"FINDERS KEEPERS!"

"YOU MUST HAVE CAUGHT SOMETHING."

"TH-THERE IT GOES AGAIN!"

"THAT ALWAYS MAKES HIS DAY."

"HEATHCLIFF JUST LOVES IT WHEN I PLAY
'KITTEN ON THE KEYS'."

"GREETINGS, EARTHLING...."

"WHO HISSED ?!"

"HE'LL CLIMB JUST ABOUT ANYTHING."

"I LAID OUT YOUR GOOD SUIT
ON THE BED, DEAR."

"THIS SHOULD BE INTERESTING."

"IT'S A LIST OF COMPLAINTS ABOUT HEATHCLIFF FROM THE NEIGHBORS."

"BETTER KEEP AN EYE ON THOSE TWO."

"LISTEN!...THERE IT GOES AGAIN!"

"HEAVENS! WHO MADE SUCH A MESS?"

"GUESS?"

"GOD BLESS GRANDMA, GOD BLESS GRANDPA,
AND GOD FORGIVE HEATHCLIFF."

"HOW ABOUT A NICE TURKEY SANDWICH?"

"WOULD YOU SETTLE FOR A PEANUT BUTTER AND JELLY?"

FOOTBALL STADIUM

FOOTBALL STADIUM

"ANY MESSAGES FOR LOVER BOY?"

"I TELL YOU THERE WAS A WHOLE STACK
OF TWENTIES HERE A MOMENT AGO!"

"GUESS WHO HAS BEEN ACCUSED
OF BEING A CHICKEN THIEF?"

"NOW CUT THAT OUT!"

"JUST AS I SUSPECTED!"

"WHAT HAPPENED TO
MY MISTLETOE?"

"WELL, SO MUCH FOR THE GUARANTEED INDESTRUCTIBLE CAT TOYS."

"OH, THAT'S JUST HEATHCLIFF YAWNING."

"DO YOU THINK HE ATE THE WHOLE THING?"

"PRETTY SNEAKY WAY TO CATCH BIRDS,
IF YOU ASK ME."

"MRS. NUTMEG, HAVE YOU SEEN LUDWIG,
MY PET CANARY?"

"I DON'T KNOW WHY YOU ALWAYS MAKE SUCH A FUSS ABOUT PUTTING HEATHCLIFF OUT FOR THE NIGHT."

"IT WORKED!"

"HOW ABOUT THAT!... I FINALLY MADE IT
TO THE MILK BOX WITHOUT RUNNING
INTO HEATHCLIFF."

"FASTEST PAW IN THE WEST!"

"MAYBE WE COULD TRADE HIM YOUR PET GOLDFISH!"

"I DON'T KNOW...HE WAS RIGHT HERE A MOMENT AGO!"

"THEY'RE HERE! THEY'RE HERE!"

"ER .... NEXT."

"I GUESS THIS MEANS WE CAN'T KEEP HIM, HEATHCLIFF."

"I THINK HE'S HOPING WE WON'T NOTICE."

"HEATHCLIFF TOOK FIRST PRIZE
AT THE PET SHOW!"

"HE TOOK IT FROM THE CAT THAT WON IT."

"TELL ME, HOW DOES AN ELECTRIC BLANKET
JUST UP AND DISAPPEAR?"

"NO, NO, HEATHCLIFF... MUSTN'T TOUCH!"

"IT'S ONE OF THOSE WHISTLES THAT ONLY
DOGS CAN HEAR."

"THE CLAM CHOWDER IS DELICIOUS TODAY..."

"WASN'T IT?!"

"JUST THINK, WE'LL BE THE FIRST ONES TO EVER MAKE IT TO THE TOP OF THIS MOUNTAIN!"

"LOOK OUT!...HERE COMES THE GOURMET!"

"HEATHCLIFF JUST LOVES TO SHOW OFF HIS STRING COLLECTION."

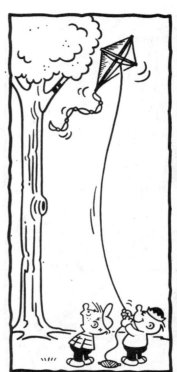

"I WOULDN'T GO NEAR THAT TREE, IF I WERE YOU."

"I WARNED YOU."

"I COULD HAVE SWORN I JUST OPENED
A CAN OF SARDINES!"

"NOW REMEMBER, WHEN I CALL
HEATHCLIFF OUT, LET HIM HAVE IT!"

"YOU LOVE TO CHASE MICE, EAT FISH AND RUMMAGE THROUGH GARBAGE CANS."

"EVER HAVE YOUR WHOLE LIFE PASS BEFORE YOU?!"

"HEATHCLIFF GOT A PRIZE FOR LEAVING THE PARTY EARLY."

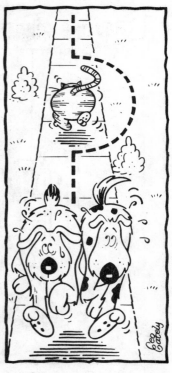

"YOU AGAIN?!"

"DO THEY HAVE ANYTHING THAT WILL *SAP* HIS ENERGY?"

"HURRY UP!...SHE'S TIRED OF WAITING!"

"THAT'S THE FIRST TIME I'VE GOTTEN THROUGH THIS NEIGHBORHOOD WITHOUT RUNNING INTO HEATHCLIFF!"

"UMMM...HEH, HEH...HE ALWAYS COULD FIND
THE MOST COMFORTABLE CHAIR IN THE HOUSE."

"OTHER CATS JUST LEAVE THEIR FOOTPRINTS!"

"HOW ABOUT A MIDNIGHT...

...SNACK?"

"...AND WE GUARANTEE RESULTS!"

"CAT FOOD COMMERCIALS ARE UNLISTED."

"I STEPPED ON HIS TAIL."

" THERE... NOW, LET ME HAVE THE..."

BOP!

"...CREAM!"

SPLAT

"ALL OUT FOR THE
EASTER EGG HUNT!"

"WALDO, GET IN HERE !...DON'T YOU KNOW ENOUGH TO COME IN OUT OF THE RAIN ?"

"CAUGHT HIM WITH HIS HAND IN THE COOKIE JAR AGAIN !"

"EVER SINCE HE HEARD IT CALLED THE 'MILKY WAY', HE WANTS TO COME HERE EVERY NIGHT!"

"HE REACHED OVER THE SIDE OF THE BOAT AND SWATTED IT."

"IT'S HEATHCLIFF AND FRIEND, PERFORMING IN STEREO."

"HEY! WHAT ARE YOU DOING WITH MY HAT?"

"REALLY ?!... WELL, THAT'S THE FIRST FIGHT
HEATHCLIFF EVER LOST TO A PUSSYCAT!"

"HEATHCLIFF!"

"HEATHCLIFF WOULD LIKE IT GIFT WRAPPED."

"SAY EDDIE, DID YOU HEAR A ROAR?!"

"HERE'S ONE THAT SOUNDS GOOD...
'NO PETS ALLOWED'."

"DID YOU ACTUALLY *SEE* HEATHCLIFF
IN YOUR FLOWER BED?"

"WHAT'S THE...

...HURRY ?!!"

"A CAT RAN IN FRONT OF ME!"

"GAME CALLED ON ACCOUNT OF *CHEWED UP BALL!*"

"SHINE?"

"WHAT? LOST YOUR MITTENS? YOU *NAUGHTY* KITTENS, THEN YOU SHALL HAVE NO PIE!"

"BOY, I'D HATE TO BE A MOUSE THIS MORNING!"

"I'D LIKE YOU TO MEET HEATHCLIFF II, HEATHCLIFF III, HEATHCLIFF IV, HEATHCLIFF V...."

"HE LIKES TO CATERWAUL BY THE MYSTERY SECTION."

"HE JUST SCARED THE SPOTS OFF A DALMATIAN!"

"THE GRIEVANCE COMMITTEE IS HERE TO SEE YOU."

"OUT!"

"DON'T HAND OFF TO HEATHCLIFF...
YOU'LL NEVER SEE THE BALL AGAIN!"

"SOMEONE LICKED ALL THE TRADING STAMPS!"

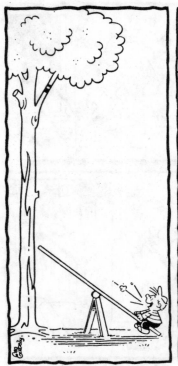

"NOW!"

"I WANT TO INTERVIEW THE ROUGHEST, TOUGHEST BRUISER ON THE SQUAD!"

© 1974 McNaught Synd., Inc. 10-28

© 1974 McNaught Syndicate, Inc. 10-29

"YOU'LL BE GLAD TO KNOW HEATHCLIFF GOT DOWN OFF THE ROOF ALL BY HIMSELF."

"HAH! TRICK OR TREAT, CAT!"

"HA-HA!..IS THAT ALL YOU'VE GOT, PUNK?...
I'VE GOT A BAG FULL!"

"OH, OH!"

"HE FINALLY DID IT!...HE HIT HIGH 'C'!"

"GOODBYE, DEAR."

"THESE ARE LOVABLE, WELL-BEHAVED PUSSYCATS...
...NOTHING LIKE THEIR FATHER!"

"HEATHCLIFF!...DON'T DO IT!!"

"YOU'LL HAVE TO BE PATIENT UNTIL WE GET
TO THE WISHBONE."

"HAH! FINALLY CAUGHT YA WITHOUT THAT DUMB CAT!"

"GESUNDHEIT!"

"YOU NEVER KNOW. SOMEDAY, YOU MAY NEED OUR SERVICES."

"GOOD EVENING, MRS. VAN PEWTER...YOUR TABLE AWAITS."

Pierre's SEA FOOD RESTAURANT

"ARE YOU TRYING TO TELL ME HEATHCLIFF WENT AFTER A SAINT BERNARD?!"

"SOMEBODY SLIPPED A TEN DOLLAR BILL IN MY POCKET!"

"HEATHCLIFF!!....."

"GOSH! NO ONE'S EVER GIVEN ME A VALENTINE BEFORE!"

"STRANGE!...THAT'S THE ONLY PATCH OF ICE IN TOWN!"

"HE JUST TORE THE HIDE OFF OF THAT SHEEPDOG!"

"FOR SOME REASON, HE SEEMS TO FIND MY HAIRCUTS AMUSING."

"CALM DOWN!...NOW WHAT HAPPENED TO YOUR COSTUME?"

"BOY! IT'S RAINING CATS AND DOGS!"

"THAT'S JUST A FIGURE OF SPEECH."

SCHOOL
OF
KARATE

CITY
PARK

"VERY GOOD!... VERY GOOD INDEED!"

"BEWARE THE WATCH-CAT!"

"FEET UP, DEAR."

"IF THE PRICE OF THE CAT FOOD HAS GONE UP AGAIN, DUCK!"

"WHAT CAN I DO ?!... HE HAS TICKETS!"

"OH, DEAR!...I JUST CAN'T REMEMBER...WHAT IS THAT
CATFOOD HEATHCLIFF IS SO FOND OF?!"

"JUST A PLEASANT SMILE WILL BE SUFFICIENT, HEATHCLIFF."

1975 5-30
McNaught
Syndicate, Inc.

"WELL, SHUT MY MOUTH IF THAT AIN'T AN UGLY BABY!"

SPLAT!

5-27 1975
McNaught
Syndicate, Inc.

"HE'S IN HERE, GRANDMA...WATCHING YOGA EXERCISES."

"OH, OH!"

"YOU GOT THREE MICE IN JANUARY, DOWN TWO
IN FEBRUARY, UP AGAIN IN MARCH..."

"OH BROTHER!...WHAT HAVE YOU GUYS BEEN UP TO?!"

"ALL RIGHT, HEATHCLIFF!...WE HAVE THE PLACE SURROUNDED!...GIVE YOURSELF UP!"

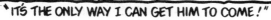
"IT'S THE ONLY WAY I CAN GET HIM TO COME!"

"YOU'RE KIDDING!...I'VE NEVER SEEN A CAT FETCH PIPE AND SLIPPERS!"

"ORDINARILY, HIS MILKMAN TRAPS AREN'T THIS ELABORATE!"

"I COULD HAVE SWORN I SAW
HEATHCLIFF SWIPE A FISH!"

"IT SAYS HERE THEY'RE DESIGNING A NEW CLOCK
FOR THE TOWN HALL STEEPLE."

"GRANDMA, WOULD YOU CHECK THE TEA POT?...
HEATHCLIFF'S LIZARD GOT AWAY."

"WELL, I SUPPOSE WE SHOULD BE GOING."

"HERE GRANDPA...HEATHCLIFF AND ME
FIXED YOU BREAKFAST IN BED!"

"WE'RE ONLY BOARDING HEATHCLIFF OUT OVERNIGHT!!"

"IT'S BEEN TAKEN CARE OF."

"YOU'RE A BIG HELP!"

"AND NOW, IN REPLY TO A WBLA-TV EDITORIAL LAMENTING THE MANY UNLEASHED PETS THAT ROAM OUR FAIR CITY..."

"PACKAGE FOR HEATHCLIFF NUTMEG. ...SIGN HERE, PLEASE."

"WHY DOES A CHICKEN CROSS THE ROAD?"

"TO GET TO THE OTHER SIDE."

6-30   1975
McNaught
Syndicate, Inc.

"HEATHCLIFF GOT A FREE WHISTLE IN THIS BOX OF CAT YUMMIES."

"I DON'T GET IT!"

"LET ME KNOW IF HE BOTHERS YOU."

"WHY, THANK YOU!"

"WHAT ARE YOU DOING TO CELEBRATE THE FOURTH?"

"WHAT'LL WE CALL IT, GRANDPA?"

"CAN'T YOU *EVER* RESIST DUMPING A GARBAGE CAN?!"

"WE GOT SAND IN HIS TUNA FISH."

"OH, HOW NICE!...YOUR DOLLY IS WALKING!..."

"MINE CAN EVEN RUN!"

"HEATHCLIFF IS SIGNALING FOR A CURVE."

"ANYONE FOR ICE CREAM?"

"BLECCH!... CIGARS ARE TERRIBLE!.... OH,OH!...
...HERE COMES GRANDPA!"

"WILL THE DEFENDANT PLEASE TAKE THE STAND?"

"REMEMBER, NEVER TAKE WORMS FROM STRANGERS!"

"HEATHCLIFF'S FOUND A SALE ON CAT FOOD!"

"HE'S DOING 'CAT ON A HOT TIN ROOF'."

"I THINK YOU'VE PUNISHED THEM LONG ENOUGH...
YOU SHOULD RETURN TO YOUR FAMILY."

"THAT LITTLE GUY!... HE BOUGHT A CAN OF MINNOWS
AND THEN HE ATE THEM!!"

"HOLD IT!...I'LL HAVE TO SEE THE CAT'S PAPERS!"

"HE'D LIKE TO SEE YOURS!"

"OH-OH!...OL' SPIKE'S REALLY IN FOR IT *THIS* TIME!"

"WELL, HIS PROBLEM CERTAINLY ISN'T MALNUTRITION!"

" I CAN'T FIND THAT LARGE LOAF OF ITALIAN BREAD! "

"OH, DEAR!...WE FORGOT TO BRING HEATHCLIFF'S BIKINI!"

"DON'T MAKE SUCH A BIG DEAL OUT OF YOUR FIRST DAY BACK TO SCHOOL!"

"THE ONE NAMED HEATHCLIFF HAS ESCAPED!"

"EVEN WHEN YOU CATCH HIM RED HANDED, HE HAS THAT CERTAIN SAVOIR-FAIRE!"

"NICE TACKLE!"

"HAS ANYONE SEEN MY HAIR DRYER?"

"PLEASE, HEATHCLIFF! YOU'VE GOT TO LOSE SOME WEIGHT...
...TRY THIS TUNA FLAVORED YOGURT."

"I HEAR HEATHCLIFF HAS HIS OWN SOAP BOX RACER!"

"WELL.... SORT OF."

"OUT PAINTING THE TOWN LAST NIGHT?....
IS THAT LITTLE HAMMER POUNDING IN YOUR HEAD?"

"...REACH FOR PAIN GO!"

"HE WON'T ENTER IF HE DOESN'T LIKE THE TROPHIES."

"AH, GOOD!...NO SIGN OF HEATHCLIFF!"

"ONE WAY OR ANOTHER, HE ALWAYS CATCHES THEM!"

"WHO'S THE LITTLE GUY IN THE CAT COSTUME?"

"GOOD BOY, ROVER!...WHEN WE SEE A CAT, WE JUST IGNORE HIM...RIGHT?"

"FLUNK ROVER!"

"NO, NO, HEATHCLIFF!...BE A GOOD SPORT ABOUT IT!"

"ACCORDING TO THIS, ONE OF THE SHIPS IN THE TUNA FLEET WENT DOWN."

"NOT MANY COUPLES SHOWED UP FOR THE HAYRIDE!"

"NOW, YOU WERE COMING UP THE WALK, DELIVERING THE MILK... AND THEN WHAT HAPPENED?"

"OH, DEAR!...SOMEONE IS A SORE LOSER!!"

"YOU CAN CHECK FOR CAT FOOD COUPONS WHEN I'VE FINISHED THE PAPER!"

10-3

1977 McNaught Synd., Inc.

10-5

1977 McNaught Synd., Inc.

"I THINK YOUR LIGHT IS DISTURBING HIM."

"GETTING ALL SET FOR THE WORLD SERIES OPENER?"

"THERE'S NOTHING WRONG WITH YOUR ARCH!"

"TO MR. HEATHCLIFF NUTMEG...'DEAR SIR, I'M SORRY YOU DON'T FEEL PROPERLY REPRESENTED...'"

"YOU AGAIN ?!"

"HE'S VERY TICKLISH!"

"HE ENJOYS A FAMILY STYLE RESTAURANT."

"HE'S GOT AN ACCOMPLICE!"

"I WISH YOU'D LEARN TO RING THE DOORBELL!"

"...AND HERE WE HAVE YOUR SIGNED CONFESSION!"

"HE DUMPED THAT GARBAGE CAN AND NEVER TOUCHED ANY OF IT!"

"HE'S GOT A VERY BUSY DAY, TOMORROW."

"HMMPH!...THAT'S STRANGE!"

"MASCOTS DO NOT BLOCK FIELD GOALS!"

"HEATHCLIFF WOULDN'T PLAY DOLL CARRIAGE, SO I
THOUGHT I'D MAKE HIM JEALOUS WITH CHAUNCY!"

"YESIREE, FOLKS....THREE OUT OF FOUR CATS PREFER 'LIVER LUMPS'!"

"OH, DEAR!...MY SLIP IS SHOWING!"

"NOW YOU MADE ME DROP
ALL MY SIGNS!"

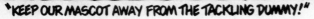

"KEEP OUR MASCOT AWAY FROM THE TACKLING DUMMY!"

"THEY'RE PICKING OUT A HALLOWEEN COSTUME!"

"FINISHED WITH YOUR SCRATCHING POST, HONEYBUN?"

"CATNIP AND ROSES."

"SPIKE!-WHAT HAPPENED TO YOUR COSTUME?!"

"TRICK OR TREAT!"

"I KNOW THE LAWN NEEDS RAKING!"

"ANYTIME YOU'RE READY."

"THE DOG CATCHER NEARLY GOT CHAUNCY!"